D1263946

WOODLAND FROLICS SERIES

Downy Duck
Grows Up

by
Adda Mai Sharp
and
Epsie Young
Co-ordinator of Elementary Education
Austin Public Schools

Educational Consultant:
Grace E. Storm
Department of Education
University of Chicago

Illustrations by
Elizabeth Rice

The Steck Company *Publishers*

A U S T I N · T E X A S

Woodland Frolics Series

PP: Who Are You?

P: Watch Me

F: Downy Duck Grows Up

S: Little Lost BoBo

T: Chippy Chipmunk's Vacation

Copyright 1947 by The Steck Company

PRINTED IN THE UNITED STATES OF AMERICA

The Stories in This Book

Come, Little Ducks

"Quack, quack! Quack, quack!"
called Mother Duck.
"Come, little ducks.
You must learn to fly.
You can swim.
You can dive.
Now you must learn to fly."

Teach Us To Fly

The little ducks came running.
"We want to fly!" they said.
"We want to fly!
Teach us to fly, Mother!
Teach us to fly!"

Mother Duck looked
at her little ducks.

She said, "I shall teach you
to fly.

But where is Downy Duck?
He must learn to fly, too."

One little duck called,
"Come, Downy Duck!
Come, Downy Duck!
We are going to fly!"

Another little duck called,
"Run, Downy Duck!
Mother will teach us to fly!"

I Don't Want To Fly

Downy Duck was playing
in the water.

He heard the little ducks
calling him.

"I don't want to fly," he said.

"What!"
cried the other little ducks.

"You don't want to fly!"

"No!" said Downy Duck.

"I want to climb a tree."

Mother Duck stood and looked at him.

She shook her head and said, "You funny little duck! I can not teach you to climb a tree.

A duck can not climb a tree.

But I can teach you to fly.

Then I shall have a big surprise for you."

Downy Duck came out
of the water.

He shook the water
from his back and said,
"I don't want a surprise.

I don't want to fly.

I want to climb a tree!"

The other little ducks stood
and looked at him.

At last they said,
"He wants to climb a tree!"

Downy Duck stood on one foot.
He said, "Yes, I do want
to climb a tree."
Then he put his head
under his wing.

"Quack, quack, quack!"
cried the other little ducks.
"We want a surprise.
Teach us to fly, Mother.
Teach us to fly."

Come Try Your Wings

Mother Duck flapped her wings.
She called, "Come, little ducks.
You must try your wings.
Watch me and do what I do.
I shall teach you to fly.
Then you will have a surprise."

Mother Duck stood up.
She said, "Watch me, little ducks.
Watch me, Downy Duck.
See how I raise my wings."

She raised her wings.
Then she flapped them and
flew up, up, and away.

But Downy Duck did not take
his head from under his wing.

The other little ducks quacked
and flapped their wings.

Then one by one they tried
their wings.

"Mother! Mother!" they cried.

"Our wings will not raise us
off the grass!

Our wings will not raise us
off the grass!"

"Try again, try again,"
called Mother Duck.

The little ducks tried their wings
again and again.

"My wings are not big enough,"
cried one little duck.

"My feet are too big,"
cried another.

"Flying looks easy,"
said one little duck.

"But flying is not easy,"
said another.

Mother Duck flew back
to her little ducks.

She said, "Your wings are
big enough!
Your feet are not too big!
Try again, try again, little ducks.
You must learn to fly!"

Flying Is Easy

Downy Duck's head popped
from under his wing.

He stood up on both feet and said,
"Flying is easy enough.

I'll show you how easy it is.

Watch me!"

Downy Duck climbed upon a log.
He said, "Now watch me!
It's easy! I'll show you!"

He raised one foot.
Then he put it down.
He raised the other foot.
Then he put it down.

He shook his head and said **again**,
"I'll show you! It's easy!"
Then he flapped his wings
and jumped.

But Downy Duck did not fly.
He came down plumpity-plump
on the ground.

The other little ducks
laughed and laughed.
"He showed us how to fly!"
they cried.
"He went plumpity-plump
on the ground!
Plumpity-plump! Plumpity-plump!"

Mother Duck did not laugh.
She said, "Try again, Downy Duck,
try again."

Downy Duck said,
"I don't want to learn to fly!"

Splash, splash!
He dived into the stream
and swam away.

I Like To Swim

Downy Duck swam
down the stream.

As he swam he said,
"I don't want to learn to fly.
Flying is not easy.
I like to swim and to dive.
It is fun to swim and to dive!"

He snapped his yellow bill and
swam on down the stream.

Just then a voice near him said,
"Were you talking to me?"

"Oh, there you are!"
cried Downy Duck.
"I was looking for you,
Rusty Turtle."

"Were you talking to me?"
asked Rusty Turtle again.

"Oh, no," said Downy Duck.
"I was just talking—
just talking, you know."

"Oh, yes," said Rusty Turtle.
"I heard you talking
to your mother.
I saw you fall, heels over head.
You fell plumpity-plump.
I saw you dive into the stream.
I saw you swim away."

Downy Duck put his head
under his wing.

Then he took it out and said,
"You have said enough!"

He shook his head.
He snapped his yellow bill.
Then away he swam
down the stream.

Try Again, Try Again

Downy Duck swam on
down the stream.

He swam to a big log.

He climbed upon the log
and looked all around.

He stood up and
puffed out his feathers.

"They can not see me now,"
he said.

"And I must learn to fly.
It's not easy.
But I'll show them.
I'll fly over the water.
Then I shall go back
for Mother's surprise."

He stood on one foot and
then on the other.
He puffed out his feathers.
He wiggled his tail.
He raised his wings.
He flapped his wings and jumped.

Still Downy Duck could not fly.
Again he fell plumpity-plump!
And his yellow bill stuck
into the mud!

A fat bullfrog sat near the log.
He saw Downy Duck fall
plumpity-plump into the mud.
He blinked his eyes and called,
"Try again! Try again!"

Downy Duck pulled his yellow bill
out of the mud.
He wiggled his tail.
He looked at the fat bullfrog.
Then he said,
"I don't want to learn to fly.
I don't want to learn to fly!"

The fat bullfrog blinked his eyes
and said, "Try again! Try again!"

Downy Duck walked up to him.
He stuck out his yellow bill
at the bullfrog and shouted,

"I said I didn't want to fly!
And I said it very plain!
I said I didn't want to fly!
And still you just sit there
and cry,
'Try again! Try again! Try again!' "

The Blue Dragonfly

Downy Duck was playing
in the woods with Rusty Turtle.
He raised his wings as he ran.
The wind puffed up his feathers.

"I like the wind in my feathers,"
he said.
He flapped his wings as he ran.
"Oh, I like the wind!" he cried.
"I like the wind on my wings."

Just then Downy Duck saw
a big blue dragonfly.
He said, "See that blue dragonfly?
Watch me catch it.
Watch me catch it and eat it!"

But the blue dragonfly flew away.

Downy Duck ran along
as fast as his funny feet could go.
But the blue dragonfly was still
a jump away.

Suddenly Downy Duck stopped.
He sat down plumpity-plump.
He blinked his eyes and looked.
"Oh, my!" he said.
"I nearly went off!
I nearly went off, heels over head!
Look at all that water!
Look, Rusty Turtle, look!"

But Rusty Turtle was not there.
"Oh, my!" said Downy Duck again.
"I have run away
from Rusty Turtle."

Downy Duck stood up and
shook himself.

"There goes that blue dragonfly,"
he said.

It was flying along over the water.

Downy Duck wiggled his tail and
flapped his wings.

He said to himself,
"I nearly had him.

I nearly had him,
but he flew away.

I'll just go look for a worm.

But I wish I could fly.

Then I could catch that dragonfly."

Suddenly he cried,
"I will catch that blue dragonfly!
I will! I will!"

He jumped into the water.

But—
Something snapped up
the blue dragonfly.

The Funny Duck

Downy Duck swam out
into the deep water.

He looked all around.

He saw something funny.

It stuck out of the grass
in the water.

It was long and white.

It had feathers on it.

It had a head.

It had a long bill, too.

The long bill had snapped up
the blue dragonfly.

As Downy Duck watched,
a big bird swam out into the water.
"Oh, my! What a funny duck!"
he said to himself.
"I am afraid of her.
I must hide before she sees me."

But the big bird saw Downy Duck.
She swam up to him and said,
"Where did you come from,
little duck?"

Downy Duck said,
"I ran after the blue dragonfly.
I nearly caught him, too!.
But now I am lost.
I do not know this stream.
Where am I, big duck?"

The big white bird said,
"I am not a duck.
I am a swan.
And this is not a stream.
This is a lake, a very big lake."

"Oh," said Downy Duck.
He looked at the big white swan.
He looked at the big blue lake.

"It is not safe for a little duck on a big lake," said the swan. "You must go home."

Downy Duck held his head up and said, "Oh, I'm not afraid.
I'm not a baby duck.
I shall be safe."

The big white swan looked at him.
She asked, "Can you fly?"

"No," said Downy Duck,
"I can not fly.
But I can swim, and I can dive."

He held up his wings and
splashed the water with his foot.

"It is not safe for a little duck
on a big lake," said the swan.
"You must come home with me.
You may play
with my baby swans."

"Will you teach me to catch dragonflies?" asked Downy Duck.

"Oh, yes," said the big white swan.

"I shall teach you to catch dragonflies.

And you may ride upon my back. Jump upon my back now."

The big white swan swam away with Downy Duck on her back.

Big Red Wings

Downy Duck had a good time
with the swans.

He played with the baby swans.

Mother Swan took him for rides
on her back.

He learned to catch dragonflies.

One day he said,
"I must go home now.

I have had a good time here,
but I must go home now.

I must learn to fly.

Mother Duck will teach me to fly."

Just then they heard a noise.
Br-r-r, br-r-r! Br-r-r, br-r-r!
Mother Swan looked up.

"What is that noise?"
asked Downy Duck.
"Is it the wind?"

Again they heard the noise.
Br-r-r! br-r-r! Br-r-r, br-r-r!
"I'm afraid," said Downy Duck.

"Hide, hide!" said Mother Swan.
"Hide! It is a big, big bird!"

Mother Swan hid in the grass.

Downy Duck hid in the grass and watched the big bird.

Down it flew over the lake.

"Oh, my!" cried Downy Duck.
"Look at its big red wings!
Look at its funny tail!"

After a time all the birds
began to chatter.
They were all talking
about the big bird
with the big red wings.

Just then Mr. Crow flew
into the woods.

He said, "What is
all this chatter about?"

"The big bird! The big bird!"
cried all the other birds.

"Do you know about him?"

"I know about all the birds,"
said Mr. Crow.

"How did this big bird look?"

"Not good! Not good!"
chattered all the birds.

"His wings were red and very big," began Mother Swan.

"Ah," said Mr. Crow.

"His tail was blue and very funny," said Downy Duck.

"Ah-h!" said Mr. Crow.

"His feet were funny and all puffed up," said Mother Swan.

"Ah-h-h!" said Mr. Crow.

"And his bill went around like a whirligig," said Downy Duck.

"Ah-h-h-h!" said Mr Crow.

"And he cried 'Br-r-r, br-r-r!' "
chattered all the birds.

"Ah-h-h! Ha, ha, ha!"
said Mr. Crow.
"Your big bird is
not a bird at all."

"Not a bird at all?" cried
the birds.

"Not a bird at all," said Mr. Crow.
Then he flapped his wings
and was gone.

As he flew away, he cried,
"Big bird! Big bird!
Whirligig! Whirligig!
Br-r-r, br-r-r!
Ha, ha, ha!"

I Want To Climb A Tree

Downy Duck said good-by
to the swans before he swam
up the little stream.

As he swam, he said to himself,
"I shall go home and learn to fly.
But I do want to climb a tree!
If I could only climb a tree!"

Just then he saw Frisky Squirrel.
He climbed out of the water
and followed him.

"Frisky Squirrel!" he called.
"How do you climb a tree?"

"Like this," said Frisky Squirrel.
He ran up a big oak tree.
Downy Duck stood and
looked at him.

Then he began to cry.
He said, "I can not
run up a tree like that."

"Of course not,"
said Frisky Squirrel.
"You are not a squirrel."

Downy Duck walked on.
Frisky Squirrel followed him.
Soon they saw Pouty Possum.

"Look!" said Frisky Squirrel.
"There goes Pouty Possum.
Perhaps he can help you."

"Pouty Possum!"
called Downy Duck.
"Will you show me
how to climb a tree?
If I could only climb a tree,
I would be happy."

"Like this," said Pouty Possum.
He ran up the big tree and
looked down at Downy Duck.

"See! See!"
chattered Frisky Squirrel.
He followed Pouty Possum.

Again Downy Duck began to cry.
"I can not run up a tree
like that," he said.

"Of course not,"
said Pouty Possum.
"You are not an opossum."

Downy Duck walked on.
Frisky Squirrel and Pouty Possum
followed him.

"Look!" said Pouty Possum.
"There is Cubby Bear.
Perhaps he can help you."

Cubby Bear sat high in the tree.
Downy Duck looked up and said,
"Oh, I want to sit high in a tree!
Cubby Bear, show me
how to climb a tree."

"Like this," said Cubby Bear.
Up, up he went.
Up went Pouty Possum.
Up went Frisky Squirrel.
"See! See!" they called.

Again Downy Duck began to cry.

He said, "I can not climb a tree like that."

"Of course not," said Cubby Bear.
"You are not a bear.
You have only two feet.
You are just a little duck!"

Downy Duck looked down
at his feet.

Of course he could not climb
a tree!

He sat down and cried and cried.

Frisky Squirrel looked at him, and then he began to cry, too.

Pouty Possum looked at him and hid his face.

Cubby Bear looked at him and shook his head.

The Big Surprise

Someone else looked
at Downy Duck, too.

Someone else did not cry and
hide his face.

Someone else laughed and called,
"Hello, Cry-baby!"

"Look out! Look out!"
cried Cubby Bear.

"Run, run!" cried Pouty Possum.

"I wish Downy Duck could climb
a tree!" said Frisky Squirrel.

Downy Duck looked and ran.
He ran as fast as
his funny feet could run.
But Little Fox could run fast, too.

"If I could only climb a tree!"
thought Downy Duck.

"If I could only find the stream!"

Little Fox cried,
"You can not swim away this time.
I shall eat you this time,
Downy Duck!"

"If I could only . . . . ,
thought Downy Duck.

Then he heard a voice calling.
It was his mother's voice.
She was calling,
"Fly, Downy Duck, fly!"

He raised his wings and jumped.

Little Fox stopped and waited.

But this time Downy Duck
did not come down.
"I'm flying! I'm flying!" he cried.

Up, up, up flew Mother Duck.
She sat high in a tree.
Up, up, up flew Downy Duck.
He sat high in the tree, too.

"Look at me!" cried Downy Duck.
"I can fly! I can fly!
I am sitting high in a tree."

"Of course," said Mother Duck.

Then he said to Mother Duck,
"Now I know!
This is the big surprise!"

What Did Downy Duck See?

Downy Duck walked in the field
    one day.
And what did Downy Duck see?
He saw Mrs. Cottontail
    teaching a class.
She was teaching her babies
    how to eat grass.
And that's what he did see.

Downy Duck ran in the woods
one day.
And what did Downy Duck see?
He saw Mrs. Possum
throw back her head.
She was teaching her little ones
how to play dead.
And that's what he did see.

Downy Duck flew in the woods
one day.
And what did Downy Duck see?
He saw Mother Deer jump
left and right.
She was teaching her little deer
how to fight.
And that's what he did see.

Downy Duck swam on the stream
one day.
And what did Downy Duck see?
He saw Mr. Raccoon splash and
swish.
He was teaching his little raccoons
to fish.
And that's what he did see.

Mrs. Cottontail's Neighbor

Mrs. Cottontail lived deep
in the woods.

She had a snug home in a hole
at the foot of an old oak tree.

In this home she had
six baby rabbits.

One day the six baby rabbits
crept out of their snug home.
"Come with me,"
said Mrs. Cottontail.
"We shall go into the field.
You must learn to eat grass."

"I'm afraid," said one little rabbit.
"I'm afraid,"
said another little rabbit.

"Do not be afraid,"
said Mrs. Cottontail.
"I shall be with you."

Mrs. Cottontail crept
under the fence.
She sat up and looked all around.
"Come on! Come on!" she called.
"This will be a picnic!"

One baby rabbit crept
under the fence.

Then another and another crept
under the fence.

Soon all the little rabbits crept
under the fence into the field.

"Here is some good grass,"
said Mrs. Cottontail.

The little rabbits hopped to her.
They began to nibble
the good green grass.

Suddenly Mrs. Cottontail sat up.
She wiggled her nose.
She listened.
She heard a noise in the woods.
"Be still! Be still!" she said.

Each little rabbit sat very still
and listened.
Mrs. Cottontail sat very still
and listened.

After a time she said,
"It is only Downy Duck.
Downy Duck will not hurt you.
Eat, little rabbits.
Eat the good grass."

Again each little rabbit began
to nibble the good green grass.

Mrs. Cottontail had
a good neighbor.

Frisky Squirrel was
her good neighbor.

He was sitting high
in the old oak tree.

He saw Mrs. Cottontail and
the six baby rabbits out in the field.

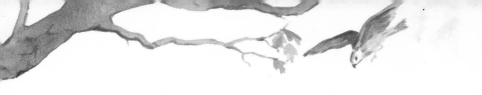

He saw someone else, too.

He saw someone flying
around and around
over the six little rabbits.

Frisky Squirrel was
a good neighbor.

He chattered and called,
"A hawk! A hawk! A hawk!"

Mrs. Cottontail heard
Frisky Squirrel.
This time she didn't move,
but she said, "Be still! Be still!"

Each little rabbit sat very still.
The little rabbits were afraid.
They didn't move at all.

The hawk flew
around and around.
He could not see
the little rabbits.
At last he flew away.

Frisky Squirrel saw the hawk
fly away.
"Safe! You are safe!" he called
to the cottontails.

Mrs. Cottontail said,
"The hawk is gone.
  Run under the fence, baby rabbits!
  Run under the fence!
  Run to your home!"

"You are a good neighbor," called Mrs. Cottontail.

"You are a very good neighbor, Frisky Squirrel."

Soon the little rabbits were safe in their snug home at the foot of the old oak tree.

Pouty Possum's Joke

"Take me for a ride, Mother.
Take me for a ride,"
called little Pouty Possum.

"A ride, a ride!
Yes, take us for a ride,"
cried all six of the baby opossums.

Pouty Possum jumped
inside Mother Possum's pouch.
He peeped out of the pouch
at the other baby opossums.

Mother Possum said,
"I'll take you for a ride, but
for just a little ride.

Get upon my back.

You are fat little opossums now.

I can not take you
inside my pouch.

But you may ride on my back."

"This will be fun,"
cried the little opossums.

They all climbed
upon Mother Possum's back.

Mother Possum put her long tail
over her back.

Each baby opossum put
his little tail around her tail.

"Now run, Mother, run!"
cried Pouty Possum.

Away she ran through the woods
with the six baby opossums
on her back.

Three little opossums looked
to the right.

Three little opossums looked
to the left.

Mother Possum looked
to the right and to the left.

"What do you see?"
asked Pouty Possum.

"I see Skippy Rabbit and
Downy Duck,"
said one little opossum.
"What do you see, Pouty Possum?"

"I shall play a joke on them,"
said Pouty Possum to himself.
He saw only Frisky Squirrel, but
he called, "I see a wildcat!"

"Oh, oh, oh!"
cried all the little opossums.
"Pouty Possum sees a wildcat.
The wildcat will eat us.
Run, Mother, run!"

Pouty Possum laughed to himself,
but he did not laugh long.

Mother Possum did not know that
Pouty Possum was playing a joke.

She thought that he did see
a wildcat.

She jumped and ran
just as fast as she could run.

Each little opossum held
to her tail and to her back.

But little Pouty Possum laughed
so much that he fell off,
heels over head!

Plumpity-plump! He rolled
over and over.

Then he saw two big eyes
near him.

"A wildcat!"
thought little Pouty Possum.

"A wildcat! What shall I do!
Oh, I know! I know!"

He rolled over and was very still.

He was very still like
a dead opossum.

The two big eyes were
Skippy Rabbit's eyes.
"Look, look!" he called.
"Little Pouty Possum is dead!"

"Oh, oh!" cried Frisky Squirrel.
"Little Pouty Possum is dead!"

"Oh, oh, oh," said Downy Duck
"Little Pouty Possum is dead!"

Pouty Possum was very still.
He heard them talking.
"There must not be
a wildcat near," he thought.
"Downy Duck, Frisky Squirrel,
and Skippy Rabbit would run
from a wildcat."

He jumped up and called,
"It's a joke! It's a joke!
  It's a joke on all of us.

I played a joke on the others,
    you see.
But it turned instead to be
    a joke on me."

And away he ran
through the woods
to find Mother Possum.

90

Speedy And Her Baby

Speedy was a deer.
Her home was in the deep woods
near the little stream.

Speedy could jump very high.
She could run very fast.

She had a funny white tail.
When she ran, she held her tail
up high.

Speedy stood very still
by the little stream.

Frisky Squirrel ran down
to the stream.

Speedy did not move when
she saw Frisky Squirrel.

Skippy Rabbit hopped down
to the stream.

Speedy did not move when
she saw Skippy Rabbit.

Downy Duck sailed down
for a swim on the stream.

Speedy did not move when
she saw Downy Duck.

By and by Speedy held her head
high and sniffed.

She looked to the right and
to the left.

She held her ears high to listen.

Then she walked down
to the water.

Speedy stood very still
by the water.

Again she looked to the right
and to the left.

Again she held her ears high
to listen.

Downy Duck sat very still
and watched.

After a time Downy Duck saw
something else move.

He sat very still and watched.

A baby deer was hiding
under some little trees
near the stream.

By and by the baby deer
walked down to the water.

He heard a little noise
in the leaves.

He stopped.

He held his ears high.

He stood very still and listened.

Speedy heard the little noise, too.
She raised her ears and listened.
Suddenly she was upon the leaves.
She jumped up and down
as fast as she could.
Her feet just flew up and down.

At last Speedy stopped.
"Look, little one," she said.
"The snake is dead.
You are safe now.
But you must watch for snakes."

The baby deer looked
at the dead snake.
He sniffed and shook his head.

"Come, little one, come with me,"
said Speedy.

Their tails went up, and away
they ran through the deep woods.

The Raccoons' Supper

Mr. Raccoon had slept all day.
The little raccoons and
Mrs. Raccoon had slept all day, too.
They had slept high in a tree
in an old hawk's nest.

At last night came,
and the raccoons came down
from the old nest—
Mr. Raccoon, Mrs. Raccoon,
and the two little raccoons.

"We must look for supper,"
said Mr. Raccoon.

"Yes, we must look for supper,"
said Mrs. Raccoon.

"We are hungry,"
said the two little raccoons.

They ran along through the woods.
Soon they found some berries.
But the berries were not enough.
They were still hungry.

Away they went—
Mr. Raccoon, Mrs. Raccoon,
and the two little raccoons.

"I wish we could find a nest of field mice," said Mr. Raccoon.

"Field mice would be good," said Mrs Raccoon.

But they could not find a nest of field mice.

"I wish we could find a nest of little birds," said Mr. Raccoon.

"Little birds would be good," said Mrs. Raccoon.

But they could not find a nest of little birds.

On and on they went—
Mr. Raccoon, Mrs. Raccoon, and the two little raccoons.

After a time they came
to a little lake.

"I know," said Mr. Raccoon.

"I'll catch some fish for supper."

"Oh yes, fish would be
a good supper," said Mrs. Raccoon.

"We like fish,"
said the two little raccoons.

Mr. Raccoon, Mrs Raccoon,
and the two little raccoons—
all caught fish for supper.

Cubby Bear saw the raccoons—
Mr. Raccoon, Mrs. Raccoon, and
the two little raccoons—eating fish.

The raccoons saw Cubby Bear,
and they all swam out
to an old log in the lake.

"I want that fish,"
shouted Cubby Bear.

"You can not have this fish,"
said Mr. Raccoon.
"If you want fish,
go and catch some!"

But Cubby Bear swam out
to the log.

He looked up at Mr. Raccoon
and said, "I want that fish
for my supper."

Mr. Raccoon did not speak.
He put his hands on Cubby Bear's
head, and down went Cubby Bear!
He could not get away.

Blub-blub-blub! Blub-blub-blub!
"Let me go!" cried Cubby Bear.

After a time Mr. Raccoon did
let Cubby Bear go.

Cubby Bear hurried away
as fast as he could swim.

The raccoons ate their supper
of fish on the log in the lake—
Mr. Raccoon, Mrs. Raccoon,
and the two little raccoons.

A Winter Garden

Red and yellow leaves
were falling in the woods.

Downy Duck sat high in a tree
and watched the pretty leaves fall.

He saw a little squirrel running
here and there on the ground.

"There is Frisky Squirrel,"
said Downy Duck.
"What is he doing now?"

Downy Duck watched,
but he could not see
what Frisky Squirrel was doing.
After a time he called,
"What are you doing,
Frisky Squirrel?"

Frisky Squirrel looked up, but he didn't stop.

"Watch me and see!" he said.

"I am watching you," said Downy Duck.

"You run, you stop, you look.

You hide something under the leaves.

Again you run, you stop,
you look.

Again you hide something
under the leaves.

What are you playing?"

"I'm not playing,"
said Frisky Squirrel.

Still Frisky Squirrel didn't stop.

Up the trees and down again
he went.

Into the field and out he ran.

He peeped under the leaves here.

He hid something
under the leaves there.

Downy Duck sat still and watched.

He watched the pretty red and
yellow leaves fall.

He watched the big acorns fall.

He watched the busy little squirrel
as he hurried about on the ground.

"Now that's funny,"
said Downy Duck.

"What is that busy squirrel doing?"

The wind was so cold that
Downy Duck flew down
to the ground.

Again he watched
the busy little squirrel.

Then he said, "Frisky Squirrel,
you are hiding an acorn!"

"Of course," said Frisky Squirrel.
He hid another acorn
under the leaves.

"I am planting a garden," he said.

"A garden?" said Downy Duck.
"Planting a garden in the winter?"

Frisky Squirrel laughed and said,
"Yes, a garden!
A garden in the winter!
Of course I am planting a garden.
What else?"

Downy Duck said, "I thought you
put nuts in a hole in a tree."

"I do," said Frisky Squirrel.
"But there will be nuts and acorns
in my winter garden, too.
When I am hungry, I shall come
to my winter garden and
get something to eat."

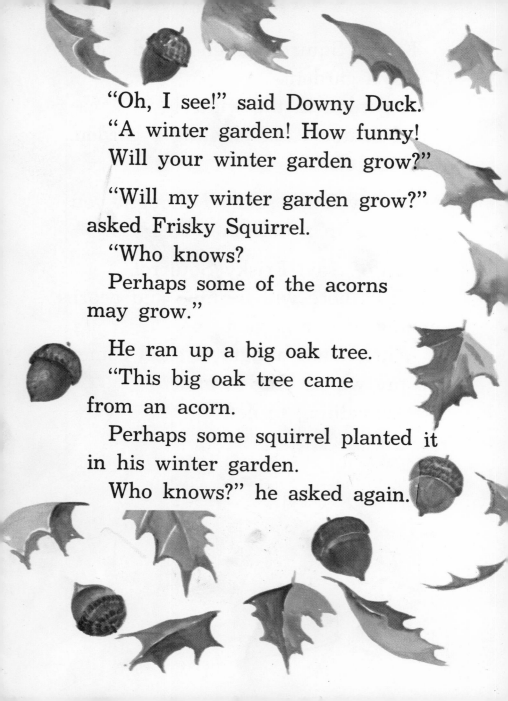

"Oh, I see!" said Downy Duck.
"A winter garden! How funny!
Will your winter garden grow?"

"Will my winter garden grow?"
asked Frisky Squirrel.
"Who knows?
Perhaps some of the acorns
may grow."

He ran up a big oak tree.
"This big oak tree came
from an acorn.
Perhaps some squirrel planted it
in his winter garden.
Who knows?" he asked again.

Thin Ice

Downy Duck sat high in a tree.
The cold wind puffed out
his soft, downy feathers.

"Cubby Bear has gone to sleep,"
he said.
"He will sleep all winter.
Frisky Squirrel has put away nuts
for the winter.
He will not be hungry.

The fat bullfrog and Rusty Turtle
have dived deep into the stream.
They will sleep all winter.
Soon I must fly away.
I may take just one more swim.
Then perhaps I may fly away."

Downy Duck sailed down
to the water.

But something was wrong.

Something was wrong
with the water.

His feet flew up.

He turned around and around
like a whirligig.

He raised his wings, but
out flew his feet again.

"Something is wrong!"
thought Downy Duck.
"The water is not wet!
I can not splash in it!
It is not wet!
Something is wrong!"

Down he went again.
"Help! Help!" he cried.

"I will help you!"
called Skippy Rabbit.

He ran down to the stream,
but something was wrong
for Skippy Rabbit, too.

His feet flew up, and
over he rolled, heels over head!
Up he came again, and
over he rolled again!

"What has happened?" he cried.
"My feet fly up and
my head goes down!
Help! Help!"

Soon they heard someone running through the leaves.

"Help! Help!" cried Downy Duck.
"Something has happened!
The water is not wet!"

"Hurry! Hurry!"
cried Skippy Rabbit.
"Something has happened."

"Hurry! Hurry!" they both cried.

A voice called, "I will help you."

Then Downy Duck and
Skippy Rabbit both knew
who was coming.

"What shall we do?" they cried.

"Now you are caught,"
laughed Mr. Fox.
"You are both caught on the ice.
I shall help you off the ice.
Then I shall have a good supper.
Ha, ha, ha! What a good supper
I shall have!"

"Ice!" said Skippy Rabbit.
"Ice!" said Downy Duck.
They had never seen ice before.

"So that is what has happened!"
said Downy Duck.
"So that is what is wrong!
We are caught on the ice!
We are caught on the ice!"

"You can not catch me!"
said Downy Duck.
And he snapped his yellow bill.
"You can not catch me on the ice!
I shall fly away!"

Downy Duck tried to fly away.
Skippy Rabbit tried to run away.
But they both fell down,
heels over head.

Mr. Fox laughed and jumped
upon the ice.

Then —

Crack! Splash! Blub-blub!

Skippy Rabbit crawled off the ice,
and away he ran.

Downy Duck flapped himself off,
and away he flew into the woods,
singing,

"Mr. Fox jumped where the ice
        was thin.
He crawled out cold and wet
        to the skin!
He crawled out cold and wet
        to the skin!
Mr. Fox won't try that ice again."

The Big Snowball

Downy Duck awoke suddenly
one cold day.
His head popped out
from under his wing.
He blinked his eyes.

"Oh, Frisky Squirrel,
come here," he called.
"The stars are falling!
The stars are falling!"

Frisky Squirrel crawled out
of his snug hole.

He looked all around.

Then he blinked his eyes and
looked again.

"Oh, Pouty Possum, come here!"
he called.

"The stars are falling!
The stars are falling!"

Sleepy Pouty Possum crawled out of his snug hole and looked.

"Oh, Mr. Raccoon, come here!" he called.

"The stars are falling."

Mr. Raccoon did not hear Pouty Possum.

He had gone inside his hole for the winter.

Mr. Crow heard Pouty Possum.
He took his head
from under his wing.
"The stars are not falling,"
he said.
"What you see is snow.
Snow is falling.
See how white the ground is!"

Snow covered the ground.
It covered the trees.
It covered the little stream.

"Snow! Snow!" cried Downy Duck.

"Snow! Pretty white snow!"
chattered Frisky Squirrel.

They had never seen snow before.

"Let's play in the pretty snow," cried Pouty Possum.

They all went down to play in the snow.

"Look! What is that?"
cried Downy Duck.

"A snowball! A big snowball!"
said Pouty Possum.

"See how fast it rolls,"
chattered Frisky Squirrel.
"It's coming down here!
Look out, Downy Duck!
Look out, Pouty Possum!"

The big snowball rolled up
to them.
There it stopped.

Downy Duck, Frisky Squirrel,
and Pouty Possum crept near
to see the snowball.
They had never seen
a snowball before.

Something was inside the snowball.

"What is this?"
asked Downy Duck.

"What is this?"
asked Frisky Squirrel.

"What is — this-s-s!"
cried Pouty Possum.

Out popped four little feet.

Out popped two long ears.

Out popped a soft white tail.

"Skippy Rabbit!"
cried Downy Duck.

"Skippy Rabbit!"
cried Pouty Possum.

"Skippy Rabbit!"
cried Frisky Squirrel.

"Ha, ha, ha!"
laughed Skippy Rabbit.
"I rolled in the snow.
I rolled and rolled in the snow.
I made a big snowball.
I hid inside the snowball.
I rolled by Mr. Fox.
I rolled by Mr. Wildcat.
And I left no rabbit tracks
in the snow!"

Mr. Big Eyes

Snow and ice covered the water.
Snow and ice covered the ground.
Snow and ice covered the trees.
The wind cried,
"Oo-oo-oo! Oo-oo-oo!"

Still Downy Duck
had not gone away.
He was cold, and he was hungry.
He peeped inside a hole in a tree.
"Frisky Squirrel! Frisky Squirrel!"
he called.

But Frisky Squirrel was **not**
in the hole.
Someone else was there.
Suddenly two big eyes popped up
in the hole.

Mr. Big Eyes, the owl, looked out.
Downy Duck was afraid.
He nearly fell off, heels over head.

The owl blinked his big eyes.
"Who! Who are you?
What! What do you want?"
he asked.

Downy Duck was so afraid
that he could not speak.
He had heard about **Mr. Big Eyes.**

Mr. Big Eyes would eat little birds.
He would eat little mice, rabbits,
and squirrels, too—skin and all.

After a time Downy Duck
could speak.
He asked,
"Where is Frisky Squirrel?
I was looking for him."

The big owl crept out of the hole.
He blinked his big eyes.
He raised his wings and
snapped his bill.

Downy Duck snapped his bill, too,
but the big owl was not afraid.

Mr. Big Eyes looked
at Downy Duck.
"Why did you wake me?"
he asked.
"I like to sleep all day."

Downy Duck said,
"I am looking for Frisky Squirrel.
Where is he?
Perhaps you ate him!"

The big owl snapped his bill
again and said,
"I did not eat Frisky Squirrel.
But I like to eat squirrels.
Where is he? Where is he?"

Then Mr. Big Eyes said to himself,
"A good fat duck!
I shall eat him for my dinner."

"Quack, quack, quack!" said
Downy Duck in Mr. Big Eyes' ears.

Before the big owl could turn
his head, Downy Duck was gone.

Away, away Downy Duck flew.
And where he went, no one knew

Spring Is Here

Downy Duck had been away
a long time.

The ice was gone from the stream.

Pretty green leaves were peeping
out on the trees.

Rusty Turtle was back on his log.

Cubby Bear and Mr. Raccoon
had come out of their holes.

Mr. Bullfrog was calling
from the stream.

In an old oak tree Mr. Redbird
sang,

"Spring is here! Spring is here!
I saw three eggs
 in Mrs. Big Eyes' nest.
Spring is here! Spring is here!"

Downy Duck sailed down
to the little stream in the woods.
"Spring is here! Spring is here!"
he called.

Skippy Rabbit was hopping
through the woods.

He heard Mr. Redbird.

He heard Downy Duck.

He followed Downy Duck.

He said, "If spring is here,
I must get busy."

"Why, Skippy Rabbit?"
asked Downy Duck.
"Why must you get busy?"

"When spring is here,
Easter is near," said Skippy Rabbit.
"The rabbits get
the Easter eggs ready.

Sing, Mr. Redbird! Sing!
Tell all the rabbits to get busy.
It is time to get
the Easter eggs ready."

So Mr. Redbird sang,

"Spring is here! Spring is here!
Spring is here and Easter is near!"

Downy Duck's Birthday

One day Downy Duck was
swimming on the stream
in the woods.

He heard someone walking
in the mud.

He heard the pat, pat, pat
in the mud.

"Who can that be?"
said Downy Duck to himself.

Then he heard
soft little quack, quack, quacks.

He heard soft little pat, pat, pats
in the mud.

"Pretty baby ducks!" he said.

Soon he saw them.
"A big mother duck
and her soft, downy baby ducks!"
he said to himself.

The mother duck walked in front.
The baby ducks followed along
behind—one behind another.

"One, two, three, four,"
said Downy Duck.
"Four soft, downy baby ducks."

"Hello!" called Downy Duck.

"Hello!" called the mother duck.

The baby ducks held their heads up high.

All they said was, "Quack, quack, quack!"

"How are you, Downy Duck?"
asked the mother duck.

"My! How big you have grown
to be!"

Then Downy Duck saw that
the mother duck was his mother.

"Oh, Mother, Mother!" he cried.

"I thought you flew away!"

"I did," said Mother Duck.
"But I came back.
I come back each spring
and make my nest here."

Then Mother Duck asked,
"Do you know what day this is?"

"No," said Downy Duck.
"What day is this?"

"This is your birthday!"
said Mother Duck.

"Is this my birthday?"
asked Downy Duck.

"Yes, this is your birthday!"
said Mother Duck.

"My birthday!" cried Downy Duck.
"Now I am grown up!"

"Happy birthday!"

Downy Duck looked in front
of him.

He looked behind him.

"Happy birthday!"

Downy Duck looked up
in the tree.

"Happy birthday!"
Downy Duck looked
at the big old log.

"Happy birthday!"
Downy Duck looked in the grass.

"Happy birthday!"
Downy Duck looked down
into the deep water.

Down came Frisky Squirrel and Cubby Bear.

Out hopped Skippy Rabbit.

Up popped Pouty Possum.

Out crawled Rusty Turtle.

They all shouted and sang, "Happy birthday! Happy birthday!"

"This is a surprise!" cried Downy Duck.

"But, oh, how I like it!"

WORD LIST

FIRST READER

Downy Duck Grows Up introduces 243 new words and repeats 186 words used in the pre-primer and the primer.

1—must
learn
fly
dive

2—Teach
Us
running

3—

4—One
Another

5—Don't
playing
calling
other

6—stood
shook
surprise

7—back

8—foot
put
wing

9—Try
flapped

10—raise
raised
flew
take

11—quacked
their
tried
Our
off

12—enough
flying
easy

13—

14—both
show

15—climbed
upon
It's

16—plumpity-plump
ground
showed

17—dived
stream
swam

18—yellow
bill

19—voice
talking

20—fall
heels
fell

21—took

22—puffed
feathers

23—Mother's

24—tail
stuck
mud

25—bullfrog
blinked
eyes

26—walked
didn't
plain
sit

27—Blue
Dragonfly
wind

28—catch
along

29—Suddenly
nearly

30—himself
goes

31—

32—deep
long
white

33—watched
bird
afraid
before

34—after
caught
swan
lake

35—

36—safe
held
I'm

37—splashed
may

38—dragonflies
ride

39—Red
time
played
learned
day

40—noise
Br-r-r

41—hid

42—began
chatter
about

43—Mr. Crow
chattered

44—Ah
whirligig

45—gone

46—

47—If
only

48—followed

49—oak
course

50—Pouty Possum
Perhaps
would

51—

52—an
opossum

53—

54—high

55—two

56—

57—face

58—Someone
else

59—

60—thought

61—waited

62—

63—

64—field
Mrs. Cottontail
teaching
class
babies

65—throw
dead

66—Deer
left
right
fight

67—Raccoon
swish

68—Cottontail's
Neighbor
lived
old
six

69—crept

70—fence

71—nibble
green

72—listened
Each

73—

74—

75—hawk

76—move

77—

78—

79—

80—Pouty Possum's
Joke
inside
pouch

81—Get

82—

83—through
Three

84—wildcat

85—

86—so
much

87—rolled

88—

89—

90—turned
instead

91—Speedy
When

92—

93—sailed

94—ears
listen

95—

96—hiding

97—leaves

98—

99—snake

100—

101—Raccoon's
Supper
hawk's
slept
nest
night

102—

103—

104—mice

105—

106—